My Life . . . . . .
My Thoughts

a daily journal
for 9 to 13 year olds

Created by Susan Kolling

Cover Artwork
by Nicholas Youds, age 11
and friends

To contact the author:
Shoestrings Memory Journal • PO Box 2543 • Dunnellon, FL • 34430

Printed in the U.S.A.
by G&R Publishing Co.

ISBN 1-56383-056-6

DISTRIBUTED BY:
CQ Products • 507 Industrial Street • Waverly, IA 50677
Phone: 800-887-4445 • Fax: 800-886-7496

Memory Journals for Special People

By  Linkages & ShoeStrings

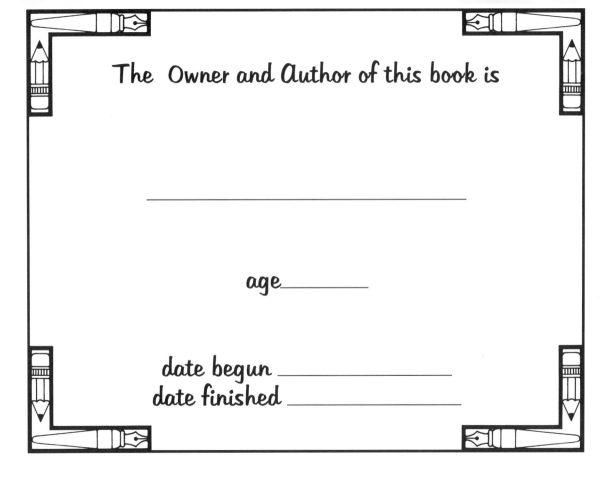

The Owner and Author of this book is

_____

age_____

date begun _____
date finished _____

This book is dedicated
to all young authors,

and to the preservation of
their very important memories . . .

(Place your current school
picture in this space.)

What an important thing I have found
I've discovered a wonderful me.
By searching inside, I've uncovered some pride
And this knowledge is making me free.

Something I know, just by looking around,
We're all different, if you care to look deep.
There's a rich thing called self, on your personal shelf
Which you must develop and keep.

Open this book, your experiences abound.
As you write, each note is a clue,
Your laughter or fears, your comfort or tears,
Soon, you've discovered –

the incredible you!

By Cal Kolling

Happy New Year!
How do you and your family celebrate New Year's Day?

Draw a picture of yourself.

How do you and your family celebrate New Year's Eve?

January 3

Describe yourself - - age, height, color of hair, color of
eyes and anything else about your physical appearance you'd like to include.

What was the biggest news story of the last year?

Draw a picture of your house.

What is the best thing that happened to you during the last year?

Tell why your first name was chosen for you.
Were you named after someone? Do you like your name?

What is something you hope to accomplish in the New Year?

If you could choose a name different from your own, what name would you choose? Tell why.

What are you looking forward to in the New Year?

What New Year's Resolutions did you make this year?

Tell about the best Christmas gift you've ever received.

Have you been able to keep them so far? Why or why not?

December 25

Merry Christmas!!
Tell about your day.

If you have a collection, tell about it.
If you don't have a collection, what might you like to collect?

What Christmas Eve traditions does your family have?

Tell about your family—names and birth dates of each member.

December 23

What Christmas gift are you hoping for most?

What talent do you have that you are the most proud of?

December 22

Tell about special activities your family does during the Christmas season.

What is the most fun thing you've ever done? Tell about it.

December 21

What do you like to do during Christmas vacation?

What do you like to do for outdoor fun in the winter?

Draw a picture of how you'd like your Christmas tree to look.

Tell about a pet you have or would like to have.

December 19

Describe how your family decorates your house for Christmas.

Tell what you know about Martin Luther King, Jr.

What Christmas song do you like best? Why is it your favorite?

Draw a picture of a snowman that you'd like to have in your front yard.

(If the following Christmas topics do not apply, please share your special Holiday memories and traditions.)

December 17

What gifts are you going to give to your family for Christmas this year?

If you got to choose a menu for hot lunch at school, what would you choose?

December 16

Do you know any one in the military service?
Who is it? What do they do?

Who is the Governor of your state?
Tell three interesting facts about him or her.

Who would you most like to meet? Tell why.

What is one change that you would make if you were the Governor of your state?

Have you ever been in a bad storm? Tell about it.

If an emergency came up and you were home alone, what would you do?

If you needed to earn $50 for something very important to you, how would you earn it?

What compliment have you gotten that really made you feel great?

How many different houses have you lived in?
Tell about your favorite.

What is the nicest thing that anyone has ever done for you?

Give an example of an important decision that you've made.

What is the nicest thing you've ever done for someone?

When you were younger, what did you like to pretend?

What chore or job around the house do you least like to do?
What don't you like about it?

Draw your family car(s).

How could you communicate if you couldn't talk?

Why are tests given in school? Do you think they are necessary?

Would you like to be an astronaut when you get older? Why or why not?

What household appliance would you most hate to give up?
Tell why.

When you have a problem with a friend, how do you go about solving it?

What household appliance do you think is most important? Tell why.

What would be an advantage of being very tall?

Is it best to be the oldest, middle, or youngest child in a family? Why do you think so?

What would be a disadvantage of being very tall?

What activity do you like to do best in gym class?

January 30

What invention do you think has most changed people's lives?
Why do you think so?

What is not done by computers now that might be when you are 50 years old?

Do you have any habits that you would like to change?
Tell about one.

Do you think there is too much violence on television?
Why or why not?

What's your favorite holiday or special occasion during the year?
Why do you like it best?

Do you, or would you like to, play a musical instrument? Which one?

At what age do you think a person is "old"?
Why did you choose this age?

Should people be allowed to own guns? Why or why not?

Tell about a time when you felt wonderful.

What would you like best about being the President
of the United States? Tell why.

(blank lined writing space)

Tell about a time when you felt terrible.

_____

_____

_____

_____

_____

_____

_____

_____

_____

_____

Should calculators take the place of learning Math facts? Why or why not?

Do you have a nickname? What is it? How did you get it?

What do you not like about being the age you are right now?

What are three good rules that parents should have for kids?

What do you like best about being the age you are right now?

February 7

What's your favorite song? What do you like about it?

How do you and your family celebrate Thanksgiving?

Tell about someone that you think is really popular.
Why did you choose that person?

What are you most thankful for? Name three and tell why.

What United States President do you admire the most? Tell why.

Tell about something new you have learned recently.

What foods can you make by yourself? Describe your favorite.

Tell three things you know about President John F. Kennedy.

Why is having a positive attitude important in your life?

November 21

What magazine do you like to read?
What are some of the things you like about it?

Tell three things that you know about Abraham Lincoln.

Would you like to be in the military service when you are older? Why or why not?

February 13

How do you think Valentine's Day got started?

Who is your favorite author?
What books have you read by this author?

Tell about your Valentine's Day celebration at school.

What kind of books do you like to read?
Why are they your favorites?

If you had one hour to do exactly what you wanted, what would you do?

What was your most memorable birthday? Tell what happened.

What is a topic that you would like to learn more about?
What are two things you would like to know about this subject?

What book is your favorite? What did you like about it?

What's an example of using good manners?

Would you like to be the President of the
United States someday? Why or why not?

What's an example of using bad manners?

Tell about how you play your favorite card game.

How can a person show that he/she is a "good sport"?

What board game do you like best? How is it played?

What talent do you wish you had?
How could you develop this talent?

Do grades in school motivate you to work harder? Why or why not?

Is winning the most important part of a game? Why or why not?

November 11

Why do you think we have Veteran's Day on November 11?
If you don't know, find out.

Why was George Washington a good President?

What is your favorite day of the week? Tell why.

What do you think would be the best thing about being a teacher?

Who is your best friend? What do you enjoy doing together?

What would be the hardest thing about being a teacher?

What are the best things about being in the grade you are in?

Can you think of a time that by making someone else feel better you also felt better? Tell about it.

Who is an adult, other than your parents, that you really trust?

_____

_____

_____

_____

_____

_____

_____

_____

_____

_____

_____

What is something that you wish for?

What is something you've accomplished that you are very proud of?

February 27

Do you know of someone that looks up to you? Who is it?
How can you set a good example?

November 5

What job would you like to have when you are an adult?
Tell what you would be doing. How much money will you make in a year?

How does your family celebrate family birthdays?

Tell about something that worries you.

If you lived in a country other than the United States, where would you choose to live? Tell why.

Describe what you think heaven is like.

March 2

What is something that your Mom or Dad made you wear
that you really didn't want to wear?

November 2

What is a topic that you know alot about?
Tell three things you know about this subject.

Have you been in a program, concert, or play? Tell about it.

Do you think you'll smoke cigarettes when you grow up?
Why or why not?

What rule at school would you like to have changed? How would you change it?

October 31

How did you observe Halloween this year?

What would be the best thing about being a parent?

Draw a picture of you wearing your Halloween costume.

March 6

If you attend a church tell which one and something about it.

Do you wear glasses or contact lenses?
How old were you when you got them?

What is something you've learned from others' mistakes?

Tell something that you remember about kindergarten.

March 8

What are the advantages of teamwork?

What clothes do you feel most comfortable in?

What's the best thing about living in your town?

What is your favorite home-cooked meal?

What's the worst thing about living in your town?

Tell about a special birthday gift you've received.

March 11

Would you rather be skillful or lucky? Tell why.

What is your punishment from your parents if you do something wrong?

Why is using your imagination important?

What friend would you most like to have spend the night at your house? Tell what you like about this person.

Who is the most famous person that you have ever seen in person? Why is he/she famous?

Share a funny joke.

What do you most like to do if you have "free time" in school?

What's your favorite kind of cookie? Tell how it is made.

What's been the hardest thing for you to understand in Math?

What is your first memory of when you were very young?

What time do you usually go to bed at night?
Do you think this time is too early, too late, or just right?

What is your most memorable experience while staying overnight at a friend's house?

Why do we observe St. Patrick's Day?

What do you and your brother or sister fight about?

What does it mean to have a sense of humor?
Tell of a time when your sense of humor was important.

October 17

Do you take any kind of lessons? Tell about them.

What does it mean that citizens in the United States are "free"?

What do you and your friends like to do at recess?

What is something special that you've done with your Grandparents?

What's your favorite time of day? Tell why.

What would be the worst handicap or disability a person could have? Why do you think so?

Who's been your favorite teacher? Tell why.

How would the world be different if there were no colors?

What are the most important qualities in a friend? Name three.

What is something that is very valuable to you that is free?

Describe your ideal birthday.

If you could choose a time in history in which to live, when would it be? Tell why.

What kind of car would you like to own when you are older?
How much do you think it will cost?

Do you think it is fun to play a game if you don't keep score? Why or why not?

Tell about someone you think of as a hero.
Why did you choose that person?

How do you think the Easter Bunny tradition got started?

What chores do you do to help around the house?

How does your family celebrate Easter?

Tell about a time when someone teased you.

What is your favorite television show? Why do you like it best?

What are your best qualities?

What is a decision you've made that was very difficult?

What is something that makes you really angry?

March 30

Has anyone close to you died? Did you attend the funeral? Tell about it.

If you were the principal of your school, what changes would you make?

When have you had to use your patience?   Give an example.

Who is the principal of your school?
Is he/she a good one? Why or why not?

Tell about an April Fool's trick you've played on someone.

Do you have a secret hiding place? Tell about it.

Tell about an April Fool's trick that someone played on you.

How do you think school will be different 50 years from now?

What have you had to practice to improve your performance?

What do you wish you'd known about the grade you are in before you started?

Why do you think some people regard sports figures as heroes?

What activities do you and your friends enjoy doing together?

Do you look forward to getting your report card from school or do you dread it? Tell why.

What things would you like to have changed about school?
Tell how you would change them.

What has your Mom or Dad done for you that makes you feel really special?

What do you like about school? List three things.

What is a Springtime activity that you really enjoy?

What is the scariest thing that has ever happened to you?
Tell about it.

List three achievements that you want to accomplish in your lifetime.

Are you more of an "indoor" person or an "outdoor" person?
Tell why.

What is something you've done that took much courage?

What do you think is the perfect age? Tell why.

Tell about your most embarrassing moment.

What is your least favorite subject in school?
What do you not like about it?

Tell about something that makes you laugh.

What is your favorite subject in school? What do you like about it?

If you had a day to spend with your Grandpa, what would you like to do?

What snack do you like to have when you get home from school?

If you had a day to spend with your Grandma, what would you like to do?

Tell about the town you live in—name, population, near what larger city, etc.

Who is the mayor of your town?
What do you think is the most important responsibility of a town's mayor?

What is your favorite color? Why do you like it best?

Would you rather be a leader or a follower? Tell why.

What's the biggest city that you have ever visited?
Tell something about it.

Who is the oldest person you know?   How old is that person?
Tell something about him or her.

September 18

How far is your house from school?
Give directions for getting from home to school.

Why is eating a well-balanced diet important to your health?

How do you usually get to and from school?

Tell about your favorite baby-sitter when you were younger.

What other teachers do you have this year?
(Music, gym, art, computers, etc.)

What can you do today to make someone feel very lucky to know you? Do it!

Who is your teacher this year? Do you think she/he is a good one? Why or why not?

April 20

Tell about your favorite kind of weather. Would you like it to be like this every day? Why or why not?

Draw a picture of how you think you will look at age 70.

What do you think is the worst natural disaster?
Why do you think so?

Draw a picture of your favorite toy.   Tell why you like it best.

Have you ever had an operation? If so, how old were you?

What is your favorite season of the year? Tell why you like it best.

What do you like to do when you are all by yourself?

What is your lucky number? Why do you think so?

Tell about a time when you were disappointed.

Tell about your most prized possession.

What is your favorite restaurant? What do you like about it?

Tell something you'd like your teacher to know about you.

What is something you can do to help make your community a better place to live?

What is your mom's job? Tell what she does.

How much money do you get for your allowance?
Do you think this is a fair amount? Why or why not?

What is your dad's job? Tell what he does.

Where do your grandparents live? Tell about the town they live in.

How many students attend your entire school? Do you think this is too many, too few, or is it just the right size?

What would be the hardest thing about being a parent?

How many students are in your class this year?
How many boys? How many girls?

What can you do to control your temper?

To what store do you most like to go? Tell why.

Do you celebrate May Day? What do you do to celebrate?

Why do you think laws or rules are necessary?

Tell about a dream you've had.

Why do you think Labor Day is a National holiday?

Have you ever created a home-made gift for someone? Tell about it.

September 1

If you could be someone else for one day, who would you be?
Why did you choose that person?

What is something you truly enjoy doing just for the fun of it?

What school supplies do you need to get ready for the beginning of school?

What number, 0 - 9, do you think is the most important? Why?

Tell about the highlight of your summer.

Is it important to have heroes? Why or why not?

What would be the hardest thing about being a baby-sitter?

What is something that you've been a part of in which cooperation played an important role?

If you lived in a state other than the one you live in now, where would you choose to live? Tell why.

How would your life be different if there were no numbers?

Have you ever attended a professional sports event?
If so tell about it. If not, tell about one you would like to attend.

What award or recognition have you received that made you feel most proud?

August 26

What cartoon do you like best? Tell why it is your favorite.

What do you admire most about your Mom?

What experience have you had that you would want to relive?
Tell about it.

Why is getting exercise important?

What's the largest body of water you've ever seen? Tell about it.

Describe the clothing that is currently popular for your age.

When do you feel happiest?

How do you make your Mom feel special on Mother's Day?

What flavor of ice cream do you like best?

May 14

Is it important to always tell the truth? Why or why not?

What kind of shoes are your favorite? Draw a picture of them.

Do you think you will go to college when you finish High School?
Why or why not?

What is your favorite breakfast cereal?
Why is it better than any other?

Tell about something that you and your Mom like doing together.

What letter of the alphabet do you think is the most important?
Why did you choose that letter?

What is the nearest "point of interest" to where you live?
What makes it special?

Do you think anyone ever reaches perfection? Why or why not?

What's your favorite animal? Why did you choose that one?

What's your favorite kind of sandwich? How do you make it?

If you could choose one place to be, where would you choose?
Tell why.

How do people get to be experts?
In what area would you like to be an expert?

Describe a favorite school field trip.

What country did your ancestors come from?
Tell something about that country.

What advice would you give to someone just starting the grade you are in now?

August 14

Have you ever been homesick? Tell about it.

Is it important that you like yourself?

How do you think this problem can be solved or at least made better?

What is something that you are looking forward to in your next school year?

What do you think is the biggest problem facing families today?

Tell about a place where you feel most secure.

Tell about a time when you were able to succeed at something that you didn't think you could do.

Where would you most like to go on a vacation?
What would you do there?

What's the best thing you ever got in the mail?

May 26

What do you think would be the best thing about being in High School?

What does it mean to have "self discipline"?

Does competing against someone make you try harder?
Why or why not?

Tell about your neighborhood friends.

Do you think you learn more from your mistakes or your successes?
Tell why you think so.

What are you most afraid of? Tell why.

How do you and your family observe Memorial Day?

How do you show someone that you appreciate what they have done for you? Give an example.

Why do you think Memorial Day is a National holiday?

Have you been to a carnival? What was the most fun?

Have you ever attended a High School graduation? Whose was it? Tell about it.

If you've ever ridden on a train or bus, tell about your trip.

Tell about what you think is the best place to visit in your state.
Why do you like this place best?

What's the greatest amount of money you've ever earned?
How did you earn it?

What is your favorite sport or recreational activity?
What do you like about it?

Have you ever won a contest? Tell about it.

Today ask your Mom to write about your best quality.

What's your favorite flower or plant? What do you like about it?

How can you show others that you are a responsible person?

Who do you most enjoy spending time with? Tell why.

What kind of candy bar do you like best? How much does it cost?

How many states have you visited? What states are they?

Who is the most famous person from your state?
What did that person do to become famous?

What part of the newspaper do you look at first?
What do you like about that section?

How many different towns have you lived in?
What one did you like best? Tell why.

How do you think the world's problems can be solved or at least improved?

Tell about something that you and your Dad enjoy doing together.

What do you think is the most serious problem facing the world?

What is a situation you've been in that you felt very challenged?

What goal do you have for making yourself a better person?

What's the worst injury you've ever had?

If you have ridden on an airplane, tell about your trip.

What kind of pop do you like best?
How much does it cost if you buy it from a machine?

Have you ever been a patient in a hospital? Tell about it.

What is your favorite movie? Tell why you liked it best.

Have you ever been lost? Tell about it.

What is the smallest town that you've ever visited?
Tell something about it.

Tell about an activity that you and your family enjoy doing together.

What do you admire about your Dad?

Who do you think has the greatest influence on you?
Why do you think so?

Have you ever attended or participated in a wedding?
Tell about it.

Tell about a time when you were unlucky.

June 16

How do you make your Dad feel special on Father's Day?

Tell about a time when you were lucky.

What do you like to do for outside fun in the summer?

July 18

Have you ever been to a circus? Where was it?
What did you like best?

June 18

What do you like to do for inside fun in the summer?

Tell about the best thing that happened to you today.

June 19

Who do you envy? Why do you envy that person?

Give an example of when you used common sense.

Why do you think countries go to war against each other?

What does it mean to use common sense?

If you had $100 to spend, how would you spend it?

Draw a picture of a tree house you'd like to have.

How old were you when you learned to ride a bike?
Who helped you learn?

Tell how you first earned money.

Tell about the most beautiful thing you've ever seen.

Do you go camping? Tell about a camping experience you've had.

If you go to the Dairy Queen or other ice cream shop, what is your favorite treat?

Have you ever been to a big fair? Tell about it.

How do you measure success?

If you could be in the Olympics, which event would you like to compete in?

What do you think is the secret of success?

If you got to have a sleep-over and could invite three friends,
who would you invite?

Tell about something that you and your brother or sister like doing together.

Do you know how to swim? How old were you when you learned?
How did you learn?

What is the farthest distance you've ridden on your bike?
Where did you go?

What would you take to eat for a picnic lunch?

Do you think there should be a "seat-belt law"?
Why or why not?

Would you rather be in a parade or watch it? Tell why.

If you were an animal, what animal would you like to be? Tell why.

Have you ever been in a parade? Tell about it.

Today ask your Dad to write his best piece of advice for you.

How do you and your family celebrate the 4th of July?

What is the farthest you've ever been from home?
Why were you there?

Why does our country celebrate the 4th of July?